W9-AQS-677

Celebration Series®

Piano Repertoire 1

2015 Edition

FREDERICK
HARRIS
MUSIC

Celebration Series®, 2015 Edition

The Royal Conservatory is pleased to present the fifth edition of *Celebration Series*®. The *Celebration Series*® was first published in 1987 to international acclaim. This edition of the series includes twelve books of repertoire (Preparatory A–Level 10), and ten books of etudes (Levels 1–10), providing students with a wealth of outstanding repertoire to explore.

The repertoire comprises a carefully selected grouping of pieces from the Baroque, Classical, Romantic, and contemporary style periods. The Preparatory A and Preparatory B repertoire books include a variety of creative teaching pieces to inspire students in their first and second year of study. The repertoire in Levels 1–10 is divided into "lists" according to style period. Within each list you will discover a rich selection of pieces that will appeal to a variety of musical tastes and abilities.

The etudes books present compositions especially suited for building the technique and artistry to support pianistic development at each level. A brief description of the technical focus of each etude is included in the table of contents for Levels 1–8.

With this edition, we are pleased to include a recording for each piece in the series. These outstanding recordings by concert artists may be used by students as a reliable resource for style-period performance practice. The recordings can be accessed online at www.rcmusic.ca/digital-learning with the code printed in the back of each book.

Celebration Series®, *2015 Edition* is sure to inspire students as they continue on their musical journey.

A Note on Editing and Performance Practice

Most Baroque and early Classical composers wrote few dynamics, articulation, or other performance indications in their scores. Interpretation was left up to the performer, with the expectation that the performance practice was understood. Even into the 19th century, composers' scores could vary from copy to copy or edition to edition. The editors of *Celebration Series*® have consulted original sources wherever possible and have kept editorial additions to a minimum.

Metronome markings include a range to assist the student and teacher in arriving at a suitable tempo for each piece. Editorial markings, including fingering and the execution of ornaments, are intended to be helpful rather than definitive.

This edition follows the policy that the bar line cancels accidentals. In accordance with the current practice, cautionary accidentals are added only in cases of possible ambiguity.

For examination requirements of The Royal Conservatory Certificate Program, please refer to the *Piano Syllabus, 2015 Edition*.

Elaine Rusk

Elaine Rusk

Vice President, The Royal Conservatory Certificate Program

Contents

German Dance in D Major

Hob. IX:22, no. 2

Franz Joseph Haydn
(1732–1809)

Allegro ma non troppo ♩ = 144 – 160

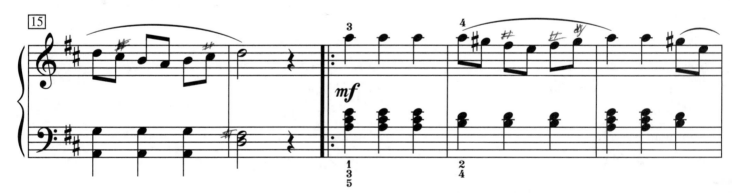

For examinations, observe the repeat.

Source: *Ballo Tedescho per il cembalo*, Hob. IX:22

Pyrenese Melody

Muzio Clementi
(1752–1832)

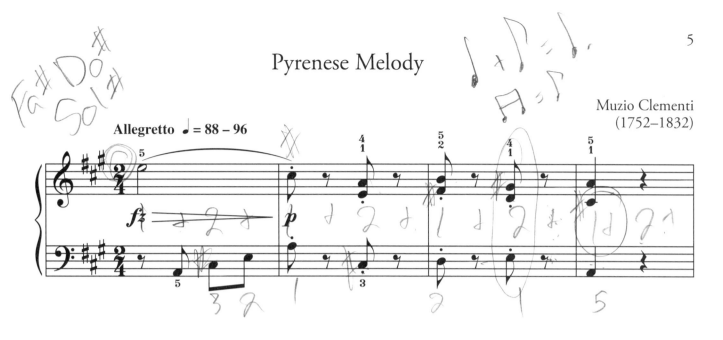

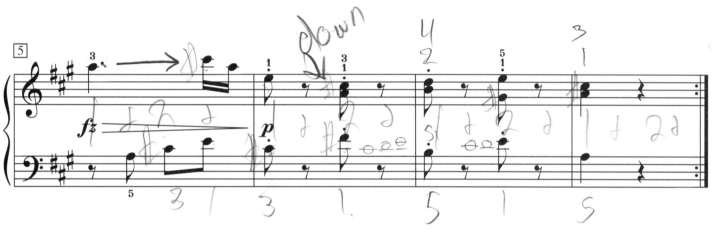

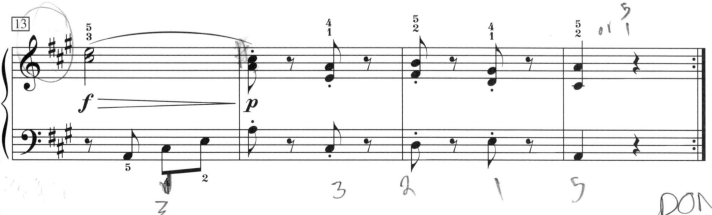

Source: *Introduction to the Art of Playing on the Piano Forte,* op. 42, lesson 48, 11th Edition

Minuet in A Minor

Johann Krieger
(1651–1735)

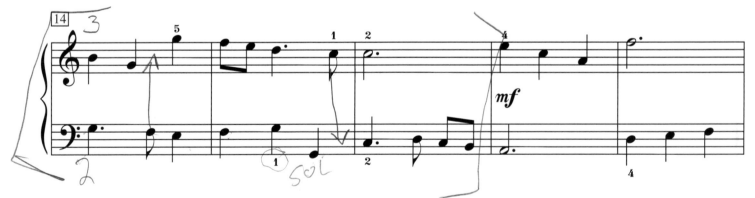

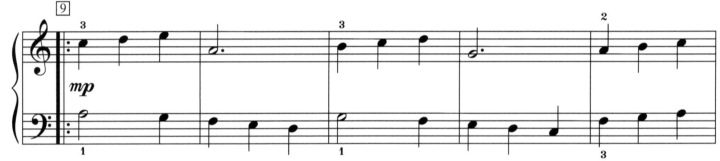

Source: Second last movement of Partita No. 6 from *Sechs musicalische Partien*

Allegro in B flat Major

K 3

Wolfgang Amadeus Mozart
(1756–1791)

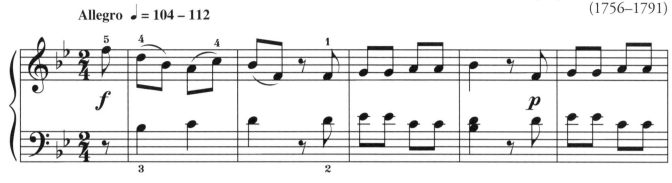

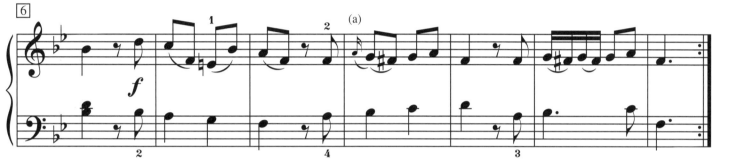

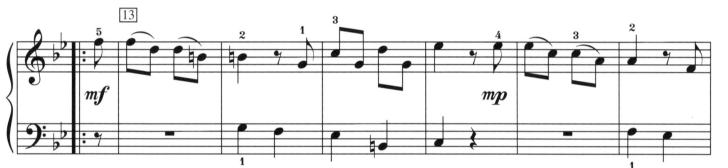

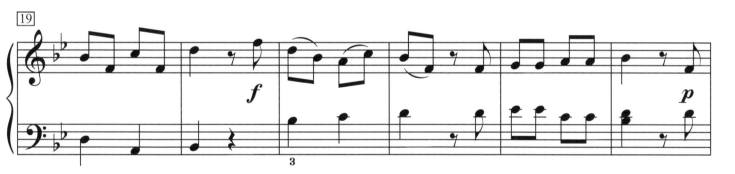

Burlesque in G Major

Anonymous

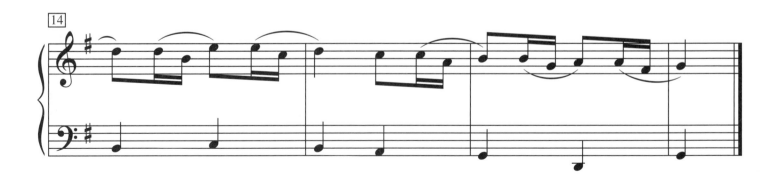

Left-hand notes may be played detached. The original left-hand part has broken eighth-note octaves.

Source: *Notebook for Wolfgang,* formerly attributed to Leopold Mozart and now considered to be an anonymous collection.

The Ballet

Daniel Gottlob Türk
(1756–1813)

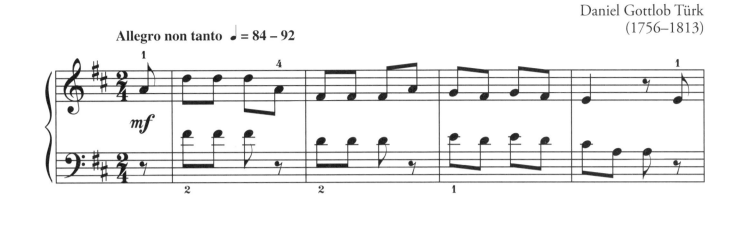

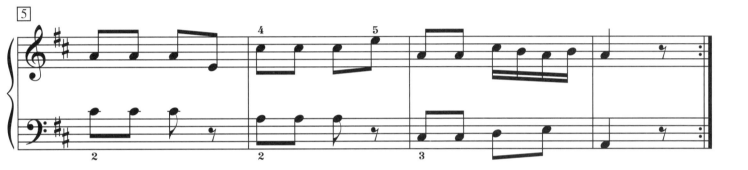

Source: *Handstücke für angehende Klafierspieler (Pieces for Aspiring Players)*, book 1

Minuet in F Major

K 2

Wolfgang Amadeus Mozart
(1756–1791)

Left-hand notes may be played detached.

Écossaise in E flat Major
WoO 86

Ludwig van Beethoven
(1770–1827)

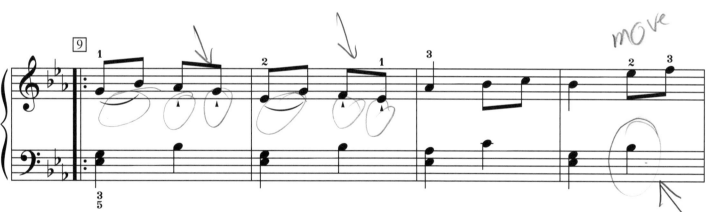

Andante in G Minor

Georg Philipp Telemann
(1681–1767)

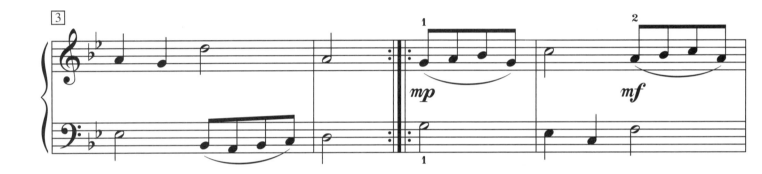

For examinations, observe the repeat.
Source: Adapted from the third section of Fantasia in G Minor, TWV 33:17, from *Fantaisies pour le clavessin*.

Aria in F Major

BWV Anh. 131

Johann Christian Bach
(1735–1782)

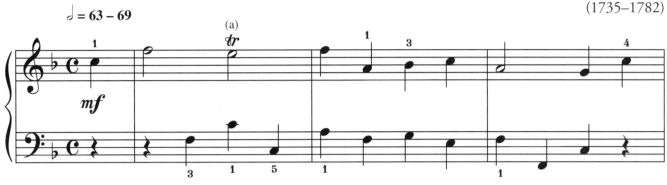

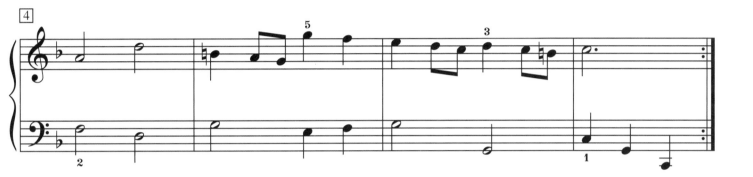

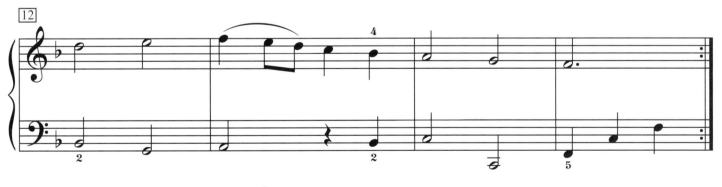

(a) For examinations, the trill in m. 1 is optional:

The left-hand notes may be played detached.
Source: *Notenbuch der Anna Magdalena Bach*

Waltz

op. 39, no. 13

Dmitri Kabalevsky
(1904–1987)

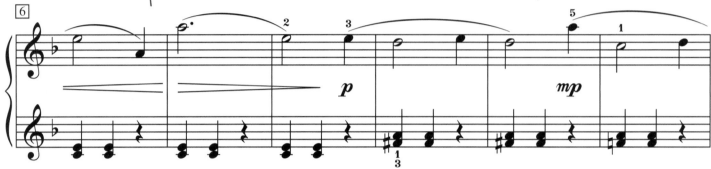

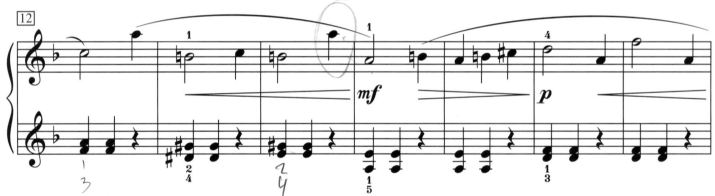

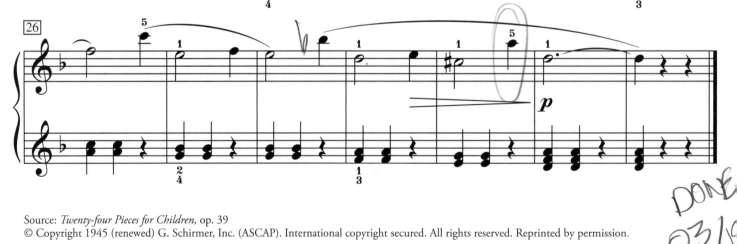

Source: *Twenty-four Pieces for Children,* op. 39

A Little Piece

op. 6, no. 2

Alexander Gedike
(1877–1957)

Moderato ♩ = 80 – 88

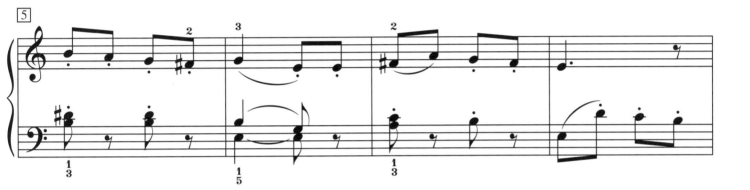

Source: *Twenty Little Pieces for Beginners,* op. 6

Early One Morning

Traditional English song
arr. Frederick Silvester

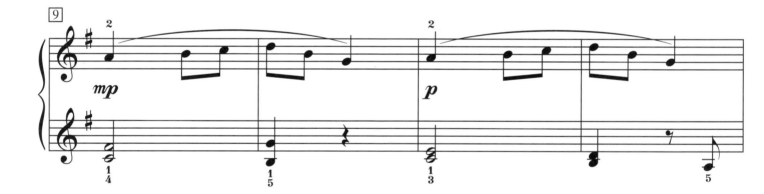

Source: *Legacy Collection: Folk-Song Arrangements*
Arrangement © copyright 1968 The Frederick Harris Music Co., Limited, Toronto, Ontario, Canada.

Dance of the Martians

Mike Schoenmehl
(b. 1957)

Mist

Clifford Poole
(1916–2003)

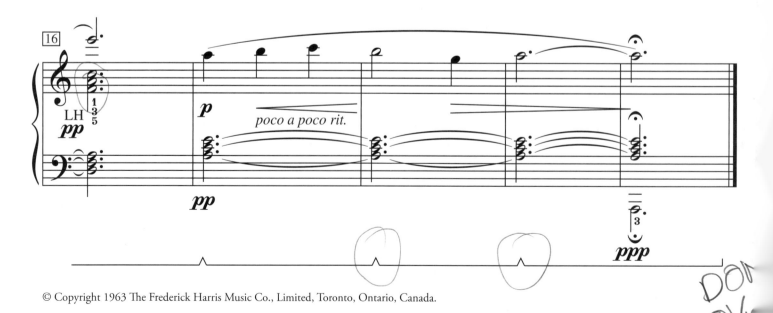

Spring Light

Stephen Chatman
(b. 1950)

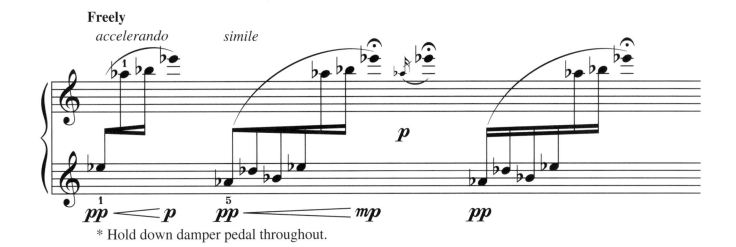

* Hold down damper pedal throughout.

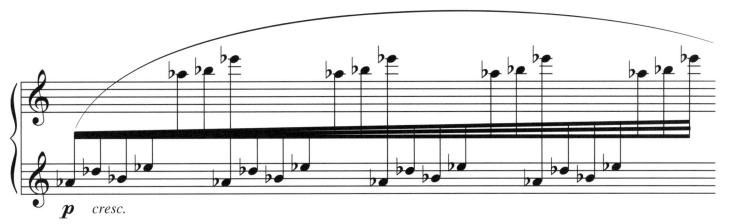

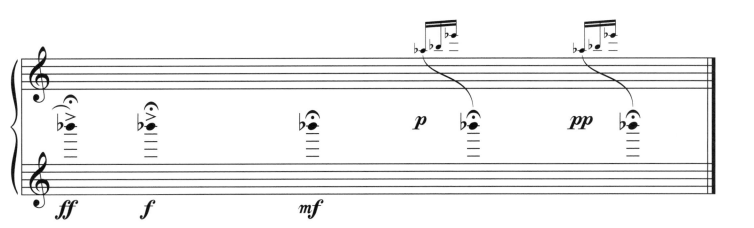

Robots

Anne Crosby Gaudet
(b. 1968)

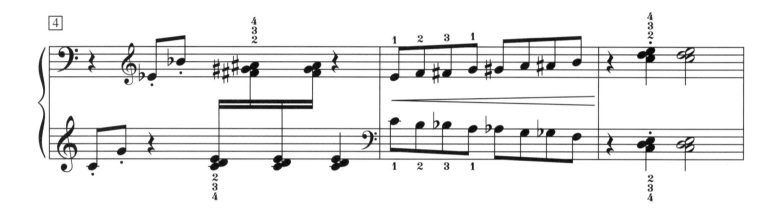

Climb up on an Elephant

Monté sur un éléphant

French Canadian folk song
arr. Nancy Telfer

Awkwardly ♩. = 72 – 88

Source: *My Bark Canoe*

Bears

Linda Niamath
(b. 1939)

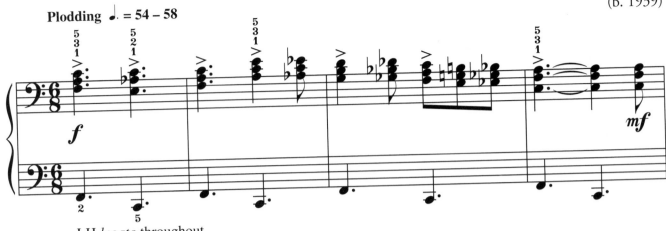

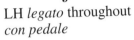

Source: *A Zoo for You*

Lost

Elissa Milne
(b. 1967)

Source: *Little Peppers*

Red Satin Jazz

Martha Mier
(b. 1936)

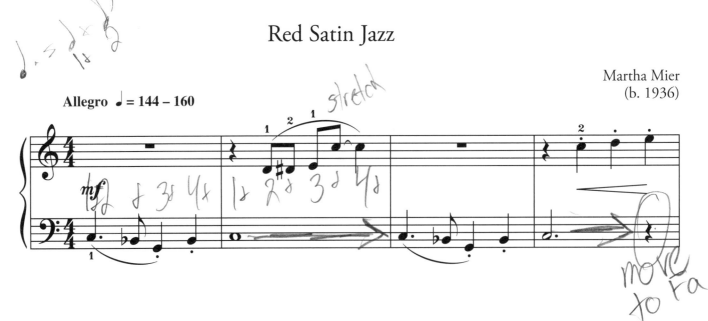

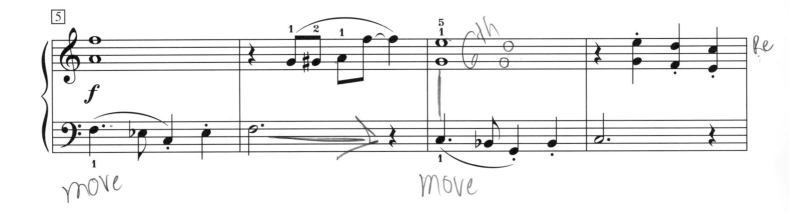

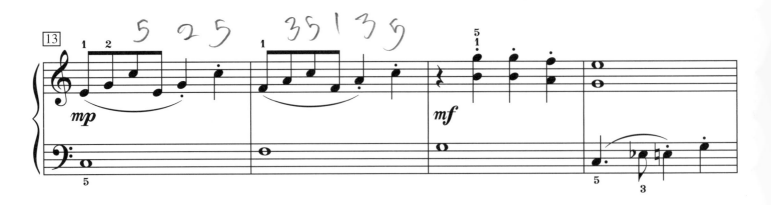

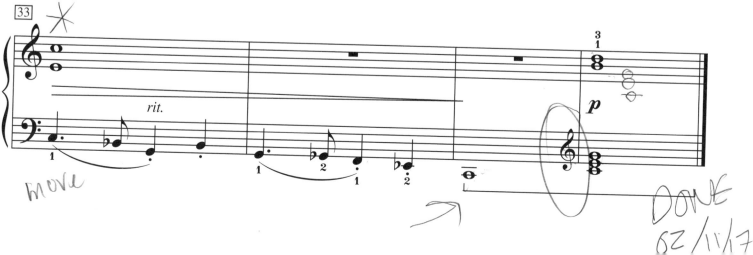

Toy Soldiers March

op. 108, no. 8

Dianne Goolkasian Rahbee
(b. 1938)

March tempo ♩ = 120 – 132

Source: *Modern Miniatures for Piano Solos,* vol. 1

Song of the Dark Woods

Elie Siegmeister
(1909–1991)

Source: *American Kaleidoscope*

Dream Journey

Christine Donkin
(b. 1976)

Mountain Melody

Norman Dello Joio
(1913–2008)

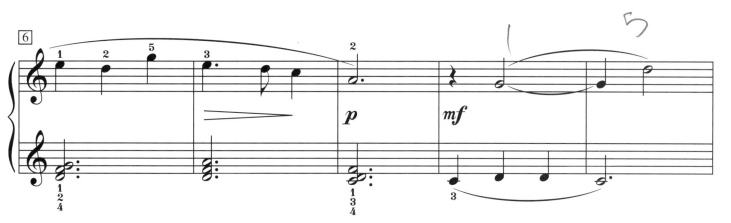

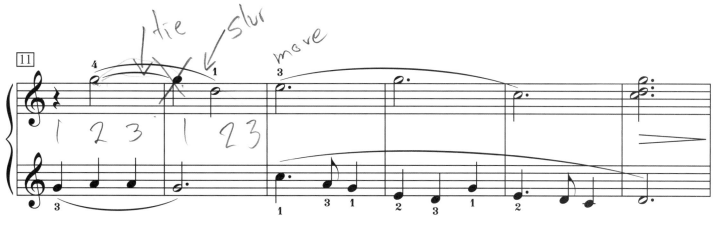

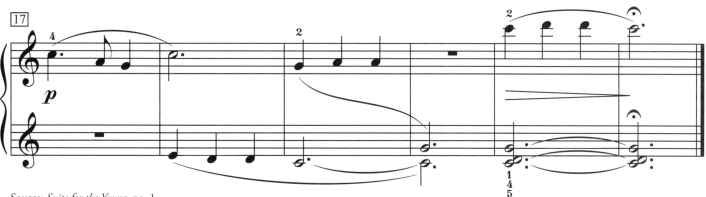

Source: *Suite for the Young,* no. 1

Blinky the Robot

David Carr Glover
(1925–1988)

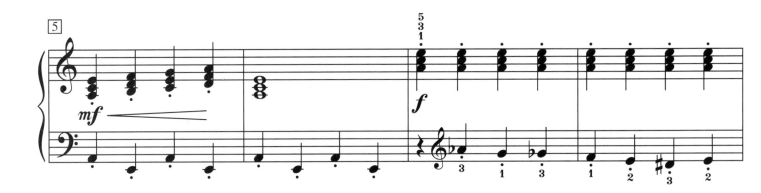

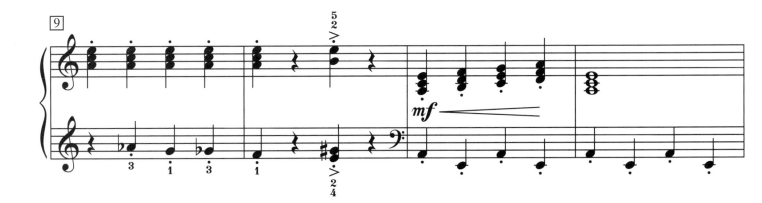

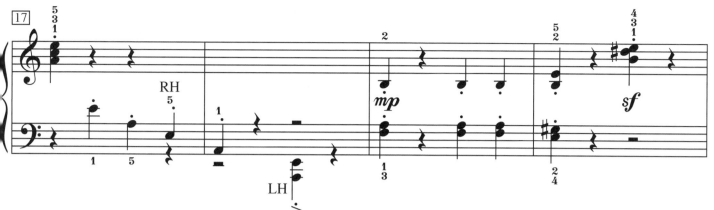

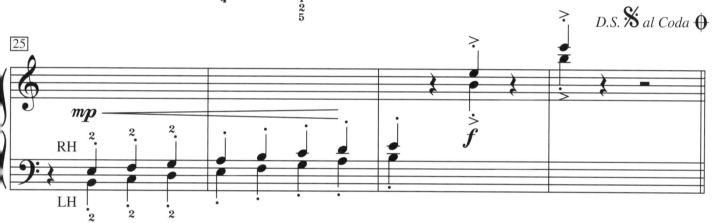

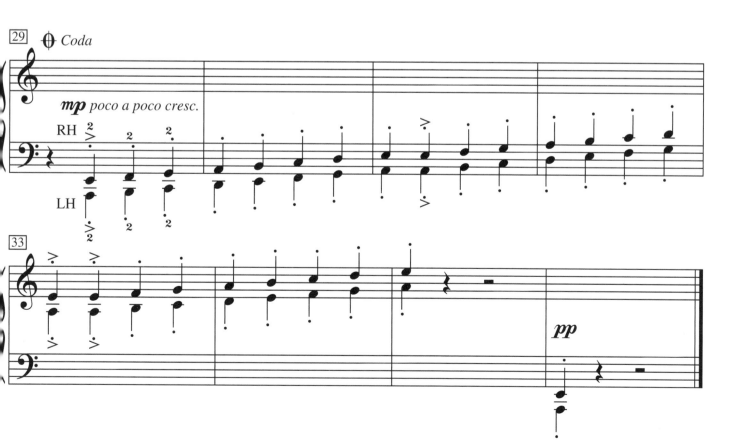

Angelfish

Anne Crosby Gaudet
(b. 1968)

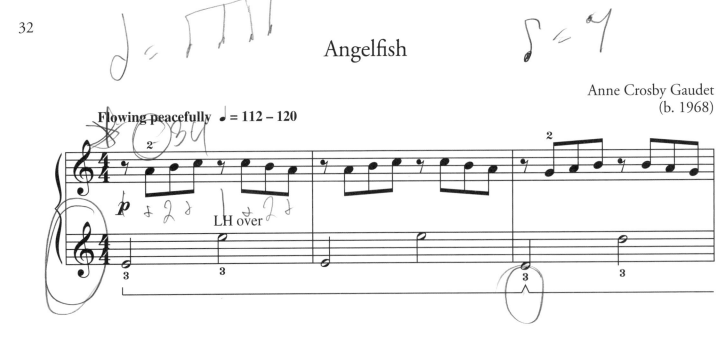

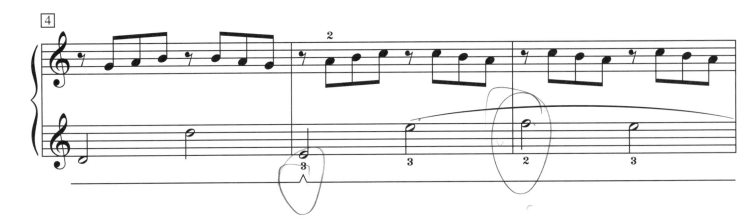

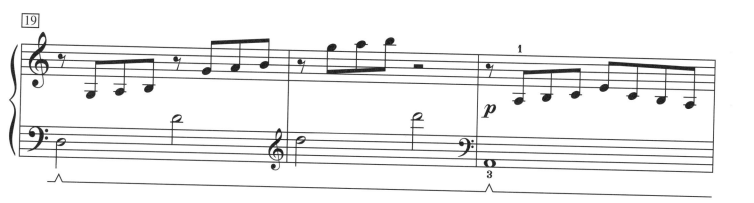

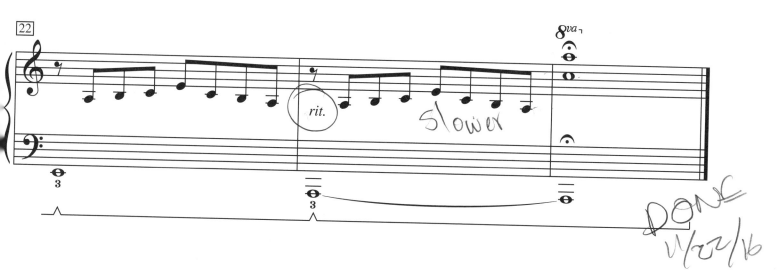

DONE
11/22/16

A Starry Night

Italo Taranta
(b. 1928)

Andantino ♩ = 96 – 104

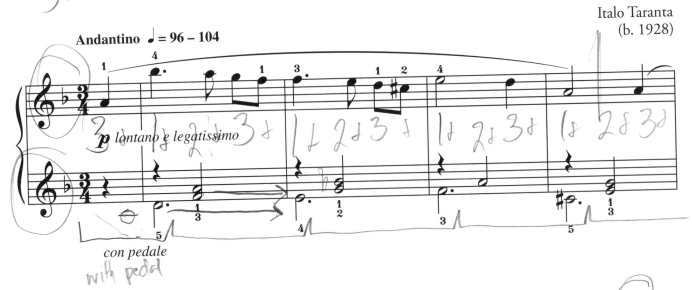

con pedale

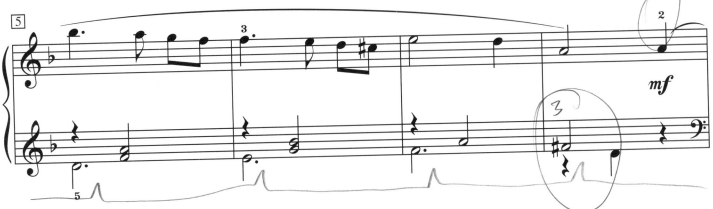

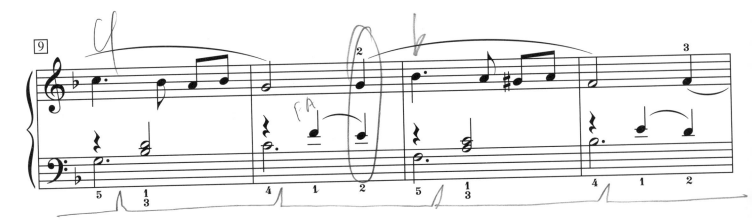

Source: *Piano Miniatures*

Invention no. 1

Frère Jacques Stands on His Head

Clifford Poole
(1916–2003)

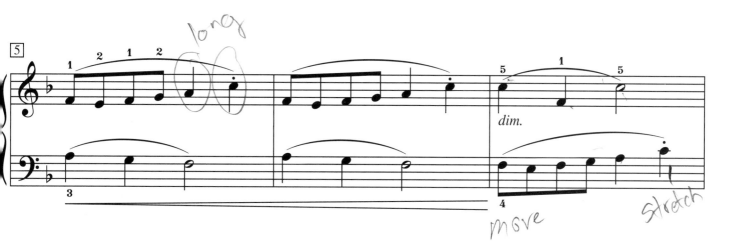

Cranky Cat

Teresa Richert
(b. 1964)

Invention no. 3

Teapot Invention

Andrew Markow
(1942–2013)

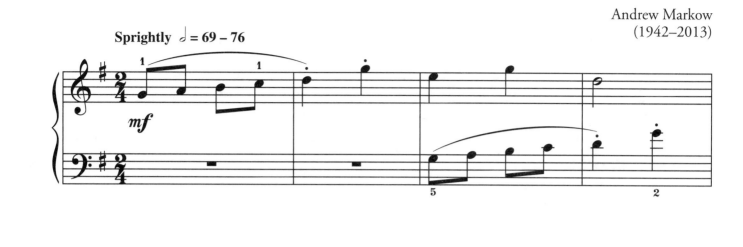

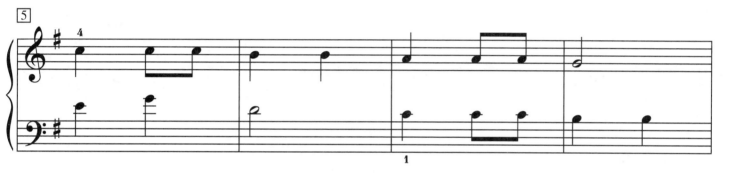

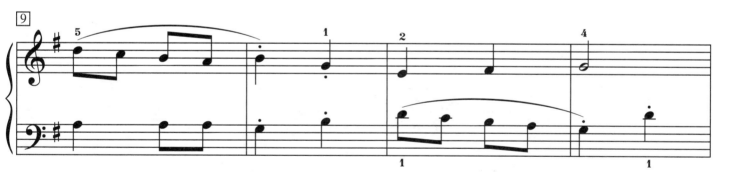

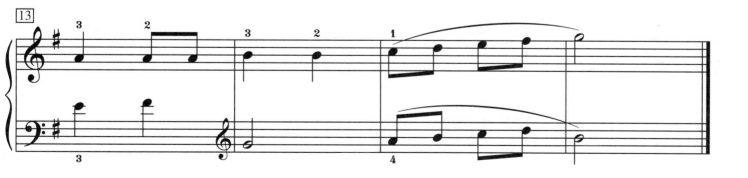

Canon

Carleton Elliott
(1928–2003)

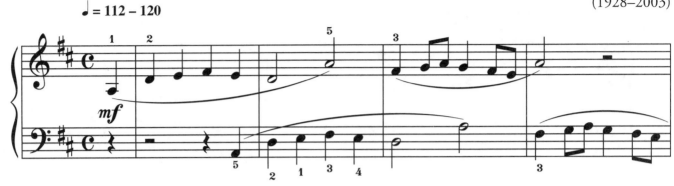

Invention no. 5

Young Ludwig Exploring

Forrest Kinney
(b. 1957)

Swirling Leaves

Gordon A. McKinnon
(b. 1952)

Andante espressivo ♩ = 144 – 160

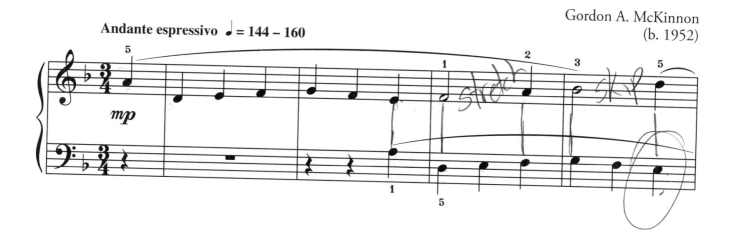

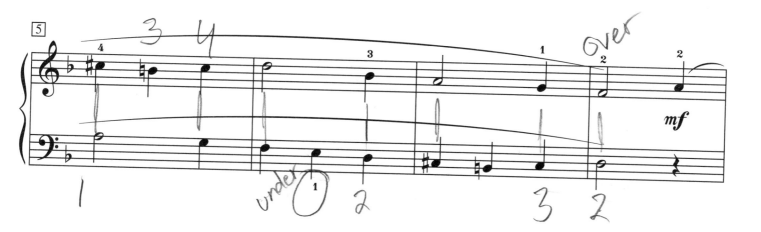

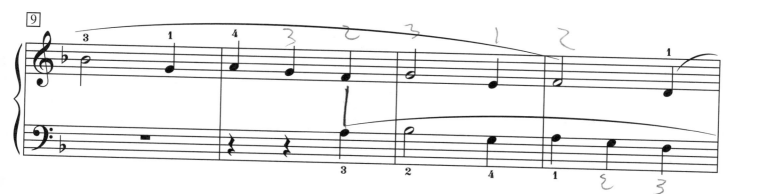

The Snake

Renée Christopher
(b. 1955)

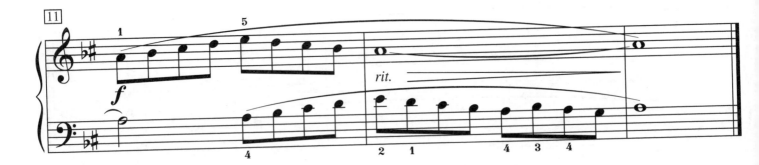